The A-Z of lovehearts, friendship and other SLUSHY stuff

By Tracey Turner

Illustrated by Kate Sheppard

■SCHOLASTIC

Scholastic Children's Books,
Commonwealth House, 1–19 New Oxford Street,
London WC1A 1NU, UK

A division of Scholastic Ltd
London ~ New York ~ Toronto ~ Sydney ~ Auckland
Mexico City ~ New Delhi ~ Hong Kong

Published in the UK by Scholastic Ltd, 2005

ISBN 0 439 95982 9

Printed and bound by AIT Nørhaven Paperback A/S, Denmark

2 4 6 8 10 9 7 5 3 1

Contents

Introduction

Do you love really slushy movies, complete with beautiful heroines, handsome heroes, flowers and wedding bells?

Maybe you think it's all absolutely revolting and you'd rather watch *Halloween Bloodbath III*?

Or perhaps you don't mind a bit of slushiness in its place – you might even send a card or two on Valentine's Day?

Whether you're a complete softie or not, everyone's got friends to fuss over. This book is packed with fascinating facts about friendship and fun things to do for – and with – your mates, as well as being your guide to the weird world of slushy stuff ... which isn't always as soppy as you might think. So why not read on to discover:

- where a loveheart symbol means "toilets";
- how to make a love potion;
- why you might invite a duck to a wedding;
- what it means if someone gives you a cucumber;
- some tragic true love stories.

This book is full of information you'll be glad you found out – some of it useful and some of it very strange indeed. Simply start at "A" and carry on until you get to "Z" (or the other way around if you'd rather), and you'll be ready to pamper your pals and astound them with friendly facts at the same time!

Aphrodite

Aphrodite was the ancient Greek goddess of love. There are lots of stories about flighty Aphrodite and her various boyfriends, but one of the best gives her a starring role in a sort of ancient Greek Miss Universe contest...

Aphrodite and the golden apple

All the gods were invited to a marriage feast. (Somebody must have had friends in high places.) All the gods, that is, except Eris, the goddess of strife. The happy couple left her out for obvious reasons, but she still managed to cause trouble by turning up at the wedding and leaving a golden apple with a note attached to it:

This caused a stir among the goddesses, who were just a little vain (to put it mildly). Three of them – Hera, Athena and Aphrodite – all thought they should be given the apple. Paris, a prince of Troy, was given the task of judging between them. But the contest wasn't exactly fair: all three goddesses cheated.

In return for the apple, Hera offered to make Paris a king. Athena offered him great knowledge. But Aphrodite's offer was the one Paris couldn't resist: the love of the most beautiful woman in the world.

So Aphrodite got the golden apple for being the fairest of them all, and Paris got Helen, the world's best-looking mortal woman. Unfortunately, she happened to be married to somebody else, but that's another story. (See page 40.)

Some apple superstitions

Want to know whom you're going to marry?
There are several ways to find out involving apples:

- Simply twist the stem of an apple while reciting the alphabet. You will marry someone whose name begins with the letter you are saying just as the stem comes off. This is guaranteed*.

- A trickier version: Stand in front of a mirror just before midnight and cut an apple into pieces. Throw one piece over your right shoulder, eat the other pieces and brush your hair at the same time. (Told you it was tricky.) As midnight strikes, you'll see your future husband reflected in the mirror!

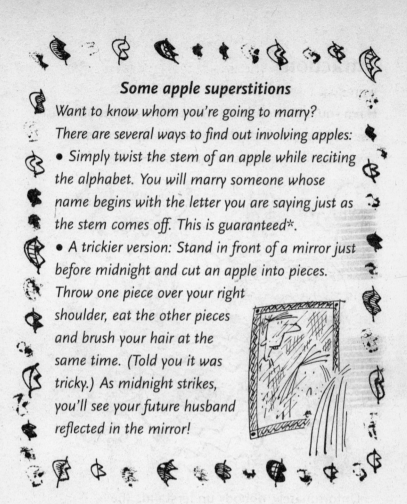

Stupid Cupid

Aphrodite had a son called Eros. He's better known as Cupid (see page 23).

* Not really.

Attraction

Have you ever wondered why people are attracted to one another? In fact, attraction has its own set of laws, just like gravity or magnetism:

Unfortunately, nobody understands the "chemistry" bit – it's a mystery. Maybe it really is Cupid with his bows and arrows (see page 23).

Beauty and the Beast

Beauty and the Beast is one of the best-known fairy tales and one of the most slushy...

Beauty is, not surprisingly, a very beautiful young girl, and she is also very good. A bit like Cinderella, she has a couple of nasty older sisters who laze around while she does all the housework. After a series of unfortunate events, Beauty is packed off to a powerful and horribly ugly creature known only as the Beast, who lives in a great castle and says that he intends to eat the poor girl!

And for dinner, sir?

Just the girl with a few roast potatoes

When Beauty arrives at the castle, however, the Beast shows no signs of having her for his tea. Instead, he tells her that she is the mistress of his castle and asks her to marry him – which must have been a bit of a surprise for Beauty. The Beast isn't disheartened when Beauty says no, and keeps on asking. Eventually, discovering that the Beast may not be Brad Pitt but that he *is* good and kind, Beauty falls in love and agrees to marry him. The minute she says "yes", Beauty breaks a terrible spell. The Beast has been enchanted all this time and, in fact, he is a wealthy prince even more gorgeous than Brad Pitt! The happy couple get married and live happily ever after.

Casanova

You might have heard of Casanova: he's famous for having lots of girlfriends. His reputation comes mainly from the fact that he wrote about his own life (in a book with the imaginative title *The History of My Life*). In it he claims to have had over a hundred girlfriends – and it's probably true! It's pretty impressive, you have to admit. But there are plenty of less romantic things about Casanova:

- He worked for a while as a librarian – not the sexiest job in the world.
- The greatest love of his life, a woman called Henriette, lasted just seven months (well, he had to fit in plenty of other girlfriends so he was probably pushed for time).
- He invented the lottery in France!

You can stamp my book anytime

Chat-up lines

If you ever see someone you like the look of and want to find a way of talking to them, just walk up to them and say the first thing that comes into your head (well, within reason!). You'd be well advised never to use any of these cringe-making chat-up lines:

Cleopatra

Cleopatra is known for being
one of the most beautiful
and romantic women of
all time, but the truth is
that the glamorous
Egyptian queen was far
more remarkable for her
brains than her good looks.
She spoke no less than nine
different languages, she was clever and witty and
she made Egypt rich. And she made sure she was
well protected; her boyfriend was the Roman leader
Julius Caesar, the most powerful man in the world ...
until he met with a little accident (he was stabbed
to death by his political rivals at the Roman
equivalent of the House of Commons). But she's
probably most famous for her love affair with a
different Roman...

♥ *TRUE LOVE STORIES: Antony and Cleopatra*

Mark Antony was joint ruler of the empire of Rome
after Julius Caesar's death. Cleo was keen on VIP
boyfriends, and she set out to catch his eye. She was

dressed as Aphrodite, the Greek goddess of love when she first met Antony (how subtle!). But she did make a good first impression and they fell in love with one another. Their relationship lasted for years, although it did have its ups and downs – one of the downs was when Antony married someone else! But when Antony fell out with his joint ruler, Octavian, and the two of them went to war, Cleopatra was on Antony's side.

Now comes the tragic bit: some of Antony's soldiers abandoned him and went over to Octavian's side, and Antony thought Cleopatra was behind it and had betrayed him. When Cleopatra heard that Antony had accused her of disloyalty to him, she was furious. "Tell him I'm dead," she said – and her servants told him. When Antony heard the false news, he was heartbroken, so much so that he decided to kill himself.

When Cleopatra found out, she was heartbroken too and ran to stop him. But it was too late: Antony died in her arms. Then Cleopatra killed herself too – perhaps bitten by a poisonous snake. Sob, sob!

Cupid

See *Eros*.

Dates

Dates are for getting to know someone a bit better. They don't have to be serious: in fact, the best advice is not to take them seriously at all. But it's a good idea to think very carefully about where to go on your date and weigh up the pros and cons:

The cinema

Pros: No worrying about what to say – you'll be watching the movie!

Cons: It's expensive; you won't be able to talk very much – after the film it'll probably be time to go home; choosing a movie you both want to see might be difficult.

Ten-pin bowling/Ice-skating

Pros: Sports give you something fun to do and you don't have to worry about what to talk about; there are other people around, which should cut down on awkward moments.

Cons: You run the risk of sliding down the bowling alley attached to your bowling ball, or circuiting the rink flat on your face.

Café/burger bar

Pros: You have plenty of time to get to know one another.

Cons: It's expensive; there can be awkward silences and you might feel like you're on your best behaviour.

The park

Pros: It's free!

Cons: The weather; you might be spotted by your little brother.

Eros

Eros, son of the ancient Greek goddess of love Aphrodite, is probably better known by his Roman name – Cupid. He is usually represented as an overgrown, naked baby armed with a bow and arrows (which is a bit strange when you think about it). Some of Eros's arrows have golden tips: if you're hit by a golden arrow, you will fall in love with the next person you see.

But Eros also has arrows with lead tips, which make people fall out of love (and probably cause lead poisoning as well).

Flowers

Flowers are a symbol of love and romance – that's why we see so many of them on Valentine's Day. But in Victorian times people took the business of bouquets very seriously indeed: different flowers, and even some fruits and herbs, had different meanings (and some of them still do). People, especially lovers, would choose flowers to put in a bouquet based on these meanings – there were even flower dictionaries to tell people what the different flowers meant!

Why not bring back the custom and make up an appropriate bunch of flowers for someone?

- Roses are still the most popular romantic flower. Most kinds and colours of rose stand for love and beauty, but yellow roses mean you're going off someone or you're jealous!

- Variegated tulips (ones that have different colours on the same flower) mean "you have beautiful eyes"! Red tulips stand for love, but yellow ones represent a love that can never be.

- If anyone ever gives you a cucumber you'll probably be a bit surprised. But maybe they're trying to tell you something: to the Victorians, cucumbers stood for criticism.

- Maybe you'd like to give your mum a nice bunch of flowers? The plant that means motherly love is ... moss! She might not be too impressed with a bunch of that, though.

- Freesias stand for friendship, camellias mean loveliness, and carnations mean nice things like love, friendship and beauty. Give a mixed bunch of these to someone you like, but don't put in any yellow carnations – they mean rejection or dislike!
- If you've had a big row with someone, give them a basket of figs: they stand for an argument.

A flowery superstition

Some superstitious people avoid putting red and white flowers together in the same bunch because they're supposed to stand for blood and bandages.

Freya

Freya was the Old Norse goddess of love. She was married to Od. When he mysteriously disappeared, Freya wept golden tears – which must have cheered her up. Freya had some unusual methods of transport: she travelled on a golden boar or in a chariot pulled by two cats. She had a magic cloak made from bird feathers; when she put it on she could turn herself into a falcon and fly – which must have been handy.

Friendship

When you're old and grey and sitting in a rocking chair with a tartan blanket over your knees, some of the friends you have now might be sitting right next to you. Some friendships last a lifetime – that's one of the reasons they're so important. There are plenty of other reasons too: your mates are fun to be with, they make you laugh, they're sympathetic when you're fed up, and sometimes they'll even share their lunch with you. Showing your pals you appreciate them is always a good idea, but how often do you do it? Not nearly enough, probably. Here's how to show a pal you care...

You've been framed

If you have a really good photo of your friend, it makes a perfect present, whether the picture's of your friend alone, the two of you together, or in a group with other friends. Even better, you could put the pic inside this really simple photo-frame card.

You need:

- A photo
- Thin coloured card
- Paints or coloured/metallic pens
- Scissors
- Glue

To make the frame:

1 Cut the card into a rectangle – this should be three times the width of your photo plus 6 cm, and one times the height plus 2 cm.

2 Fold the card into three equal parts.

3 Cut a window out of the middle part of the card leaving a 2 cm border.

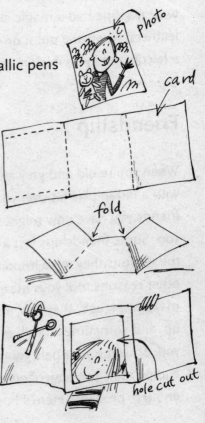

4 Decorate the border with the pens or paints – simple swirls or stars are easy and look especially good in gold or silver ink. Or you could draw or write something appropriate to your friend.

5 Turn the card over so the decorated side of the border is face down. Glue the photo onto the first part of the card, then glue the border in the middle part.

6 Fold the glued border over the photo to give you your frame.

7 You now have a photo-frame card. Write a message to your friend inside.

Here's another good idea to show your mates how much you appreciate them: compile a CD of songs you think they'll like.

Some unfriendly superstitions

If a friend gives you a knife as a present, the friendship will end unless you give your friend a coin in return. (Though why a friend would want to give you a knife as a present is anybody's guess.) Another superstition says that if you spill pepper you'll have a big row with your best mate.

How good a friend are you?

Where are you on the Good Pal Gauge? Try this friendship test and find out...

1 When was the last time you did anything special for your best friend?

a) On their birthday.

b) Last week – you usually do something special every so often.

c) You forgot their birthday, but remembered to send a Christmas card ... once.

2 One of your friends has just told you they're in love with the geekiest boy/girl in the school. Do you...?

a) Laugh loudly, tell them to forget it or risk geekdom themselves, and then tell all your other friends about it – it's too funny to keep to yourself.

b) Tell them you think he/she seems really nice and tell yourself it takes all kinds ... and anyway he might be really nice.

c) Tell them you think he/she's a geek but promise to keep their dark secret.

3 Your mate's having trouble with their maths homework. You're a maths whiz. Do you....?

a) Do nothing. We can't all be good at everything, can we?

b) Be sympathetic but don't give any help.

c) Go through the maths with them until they understand.

4 Your friend starts seeing a lot of a girl/boy you can't stand. Do you...?

a) Tell your friend they have a choice: it's either you or Miss/Mr Irritating.

b) Decide that if your mate likes this person they can't be all bad and try to get to know your mate's new pal a bit better.

c) Only see your friend when that horrible girl/boy isn't around.

5 Your friend phones asking if they can borrow your brand-new top. You haven't even worn it yourself yet, and the last time they borrowed something they spilled blackcurrant juice all over it. Do you...?

a) Say yes.

b) Say yes, but warn them that if they ruin it you will tell everyone about geek boy/girl.

c) Say no.

6 Do you ever spend hours talking to your friend on the phone even though you've just spent all day at school with them?
a) Yes, all the time.
b) Sometimes – if there's some really juicy gossip.
c) No.

7 Your mate has forgotten their lunch money. You only have enough for your own lunch. Do you...?
a) Offer to help ask around to see if anyone else has some spare cash.
b) Offer to share yours with them.
c) Offer to let them watch you eat your lunch.

8 Crusher Smith, well-known nutter, has started picking on your friend recently. What do you do?
a) Stand up to Crusher with your mate the next time there's any bother.

b) Sympathize with your friend but don't get involved. What can you do?
c) Get away from your (ex-)friend as soon as possible. You could be next!

Add up your score
1 a) 5 **b)** 10 **c)** 0; **2 a)** 0 **b)** 10 **c)** 5; **3 a)** 0 **b)** 5 **c)** 10;
4 a) 0 **b)** 10 **c)** 5; **5 a)** 10 **b)** 5 **c)** 0; **6 a)** 10 **b)** 5 **c)** 0;
7 a) 5 **b)** 10 **c)** 0; **8 a)** 10 **b)** 5 **c)** 0

More than 65
You're a true friend who really appreciates pals, stands up for them and helps them out in times of trouble. Award yourself your favourite treat (which you'll probably want to share with a mate).

40–65
You're not a bad mate, but there's definitely room for improvement. Get some of your pals round for a sleepover, lavish them with gifts and pizza and learn to appreciate them even more.

Less than 40
Go and give your best friend a bunch of flowers, their favourite chocolate bar and an apology – immediately! You're not being much of a pal at the moment so you need to start changing your ways.

Games

Here are a few games that are great for sleepovers (see page 69) ... or any time you want to have fun with your friends.

Dice with danger

You need:
- Two dice
- A packet of cream crackers
- A jar of mustard
- A few teaspoons
- A jar of jam
- A pair of (clean) knickers
- A bowl of ice cubes
- A glass of water (for gargling)

To play:
Simply roll the dice, then perform the dreadfully dangerous task that corresponds with the total number you throw:

1 Put two ice cubes down your top.

2 Do a cartwheel.

3 Decorate your face with jam – at least two teaspoons of it.

4 Eat three cream crackers without having a drink.

5 Dance around the room with a pair of knickers on your head.

6 Gargle the national anthem.

7 Do an impression of your head teacher.

8 Eat half a teaspoon of mustard.

9 Do a handstand.

10 Sing "Heads, Shoulders, Knees and Toes" and do all the actions.

11 Pretend to be a chimp.

12 Put an ice cube on your head and leave it there till it melts.

You could turn this into a game of "Truth or Dare?". Offer each player the choice of either performing the task or telling the truth in answer to any question you ask them. Be warned, though: it can all get a bit emotional!

Mirrorless makeover

You need:
Lots of different
kinds of
make-up.
To play:
Give
everyone a
time limit
of fifteen
minutes to
make
themselves look
gorgeous with the

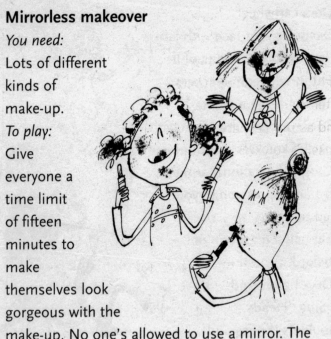

make-up. No one's allowed to use a mirror. The
funniest result wins! (Tip: it's a good idea to have a
camera handy for this one.)

Consequences

This game can be hilariously funny. It's best with at
least four players.
You need:
Sheets of paper and pens for everyone.
To play:
1 Sit in a circle.

2 On each piece of paper, everyone should write the headings shown on the right, leaving some space after the first three lines and as much space as possible after the next three:

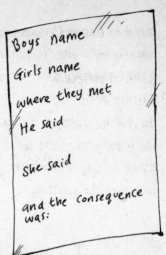

Boys name
Girls name
where they met
He said

She said

and the consequence was:

3 Everyone has to fill in a boy's name, then fold the paper over so the name is obscured.

4 Pass the paper to the player on your right. Now fill in a girl's name, fold the paper over and pass it on again ... and so on. The boy and girl can be anybody you like – someone you know, the Prime Minister, a famous actress ... they don't have to be still alive, or even real people. (You could have your best friend, Sharon from *EastEnders*, George W Bush, Napoleon or Rodney Snodgrass from number 38.) They might meet in a romantic restaurant, in a ditch, at a bus stop ... anywhere you can think of, the sillier the better. Perhaps one of them could use a terrible chat-up line (see page 16), but again they can say anything you like – it's funniest if you make your girl answer your boy even though it won't end up on the same piece of paper. Consequences can range from living happily ever after to joining a circus or falling off a cliff.

5 When you've all finished writing your consequences, pass the paper on again. Each person reads out their piece of paper. The results can be side-splitting!

Helen and Paris

Remember the story of Aphrodite and the golden apple from page 9? Here's what happened next...

Aphrodite had promised Paris the world's most beautiful woman, whose name was Helen. But there was a slight hitch: Helen was married to Menelaus, the King of Sparta.

Paris, a young, handsome prince of the great city of Troy, decided to pay Sparta a visit. He was welcomed into the palace by Menelaus and Helen, who were the perfect hosts to their royal 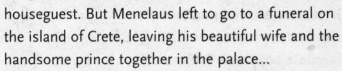 houseguest. But Menelaus left to go to a funeral on the island of Crete, leaving his beautiful wife and the handsome prince together in the palace...

Well, one thing led to another and before you knew it Helen and Paris were running off to Troy together. Then, conveniently ignoring the fact that Helen already had a husband, the two of them got married.

As you might imagine, Menelaus soon arrived in Troy looking for Helen. And he'd brought with him his brother Agamemnon and the entire Greek fleet, heavily armed and not looking very friendly. The Trojan War raged for ten years before the Greeks finally beat the Trojans.

Menelaus said that he was going to kill Helen after the War, but ended up taking her home with him instead ... though they probably didn't live happily ever after.

Ishtar

Ishtar was an important and powerful goddess of love in the ancient civilization of Babylon. Her favourite boyfriend, Tammuz, was also her son (well, it takes all kinds). Rather like Orpheus (see page 55), Ishtar went down to the Underworld to try and get Tammuz back from the dead after he'd been killed, but she didn't succeed and had to live without him.

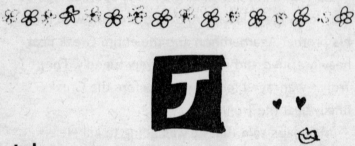

Jokes

If love stories aren't really your thing, why not crack a few jokes instead? They're guaranteed to wipe a slushy smile off anyone's face!

What did one candle say to the other?
Would you go out with me tonight?

What did the zombie's friends say when he introduced his girlfriend?
Where did you dig her up?

What noise do porcupines make when they kiss?
Ouch!

What did the cook give his girlfriend when he asked her to marry him?
A fourteen-carrot onion ring.

What happened to the couple who met in a revolving door?
They're still going around together.

What do you call a hippy's wife?
Mississippi.

Why was the jellyfish dumped by his girlfriend?
He stung her into action.

Kissing

There are many different types of kiss, from the brief peck delivered by an auntie to a full snog. In different cultures there are different amounts of kissing. In many European countries it's very common to kiss complete strangers as a way of saying hello and goodbye. As a greeting, posh people often kiss the air instead of the other person's cheek, while making a "mwa!" sound – practise this with your friends for when you're older and holding posh cocktail parties.

Full snogging should be a private affair, and yet it's quite common to see people canoodling at the bus stop, in restaurants or just about anywhere. In medieval Italy, a couple kissing in public could be forced to marry one another!

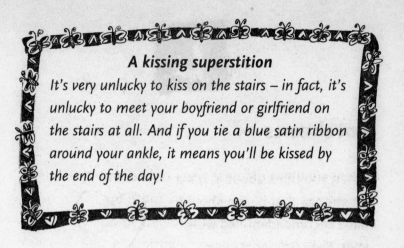

A kissing superstition

It's very unlucky to kiss on the stairs – in fact, it's unlucky to meet your boyfriend or girlfriend on the stairs at all. And if you tie a blue satin ribbon around your ankle, it means you'll be kissed by the end of the day!

Some slushy kissing facts

The world's longest kiss was performed by an Italian couple on 14 February 2004. It lasted a lip-shrivelling 31 hours and 18 minutes. The man had to be given oxygen afterwards! On the same date another kissing record was set: 5,122 Philippine couples kissed at midnight, breaking the world record for simultaneous kissing.

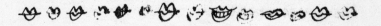

Lovehearts

When you think about it, it's a
bit strange that hearts should
have become identified with
love. The traditional heart
shape is like this:
But in fact hearts are blobby,
squishy things with gruesome
valves sticking out of them.
They wouldn't look quite as
nice decorating valentine's
cards, would they?

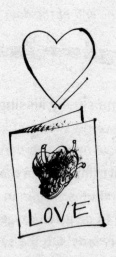

   The heart shape has been used by different
people all over the world, and for thousands of years
– the first example we know about was drawn by a
hunter just before the Ice Age! It's had many
different meanings. The Victorians were very keen
on using the heart shape as a sign of love, and
they're at least partly responsible for how popular
the symbol is today.

A loveheart fact

In Sweden, the heart symbol used to be a sign for mixed-sex toilets!

Love letters

People in love tend to send messages to their beloved any time they're apart – even if it's only for five minutes. Love letters have always been popular and now love emails and love texts have become popular too.

♥ ♥ *TRUE LOVE STORIES: Napoleon and Josephine*

Some of the most famous love letters ever written were from the French general Napoleon to his wife Josephine.

Josephine was a beautiful aristocrat who had narrowly missed losing her head in the French Revolution (when all the posh people were guillotined). She and Napoleon met and were married in 1796, though Josephine doesn't seem to have been all that bothered about Napoleon – she was more interested in the fact that he was very powerful and could protect her and her two children. (Her previous husband had lost his head in the French Revolution – you can see why she might have been a little jumpy.) While Napoleon was off with his army fighting battles and being famous, he wrote truck-loads of love letters to his wife from the battlefield. Here are just a few lines from some of them:

Each day since I knew you I have adored you yet more and more....

It is not in my power to have a single thought that is not of you.

A million hot kisses burning like the equator...

Bleurgh!

But while Josephine was receiving Napoleon's passionate letters, she was also seeing loads of other boyfriends! An army officer told Napoleon what Josephine was up to, and he stopped sending letters and started being very angry indeed. The tables were turned: now Napoleon started seeing other girlfriends and Josephine was miserable. Eventually, the two of them were divorced.

Charlotte's love letters

The Victorian writer Charlotte Brontë fell in love with her German teacher and sent him love letters. But instead of tying them up in pink ribbon and keeping them for ever (or whatever you're supposed to do), the German teacher ripped them into pieces and threw them straight in the bin – perhaps because he was already married to someone else. His wife spotted the torn-up letters and, in the days before handy things like sticky tape, she stitched them back together with needle and thread. The stitched-up letters still exist – you can see them in the British Library in London.

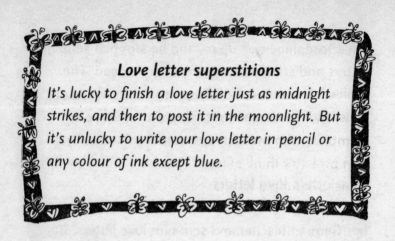

Love letter superstitions

It's lucky to finish a love letter just as midnight strikes, and then to post it in the moonlight. But it's unlucky to write your love letter in pencil or any colour of ink except blue.

Love potions
See *Potions*.

Love tokens
See *Tokens*.

Marriage
See *Weddings*.

Music

"Love" is the most likely word to appear in a song title. There are millions of songs about love, complete with the slushiest words possible – you can probably think of loads. But here are a few love songs you might not have heard of...

● Henry VIII is supposed to have written a love song: "Greensleeves", a tune popular with recorder players. It has some soppy Tudor lyrics that start off...

Alas, my love, you do me wrong
To cast me off discourteously

... and don't get much better as they go on. It's said that he wrote it for his second wife, Anne Boleyn, who was fond of outfits with green sleeves – wonder if he wrote it before or after he had her head cut off?

- One of the silliest love songs of all time must be "Yummy, Yummy, Yummy (I've Got Love in My Tummy)" by Ohio Express, released in 1968.

- Another close contender for silliest love song ever was sung by Debbie Reynolds more than 50 years ago: "Abba Dabba Honeymoon" features the lyrics "Abba dabba dabba dabba dabba dabba dabba". It means "Chimp, I love you too" in chimp language – of course!

Nelson

In case you're wondering what a one-eyed, one-armed war hero is doing in a book about love, it's because of his famous love affair...

♥ ♥ TRUE LOVE STORIES: Lord Nelson and Lady Hamilton

Lord Horatio Nelson was a brave sea admiral. Lady Emma Hamilton was a famous beauty. When they met it was ... love at first sight. The only things standing in their way were Lady Hamilton's husband, William, and Lord Nelson's wife, Fanny. Luckily, William Hamilton, an older man fond of collecting antique vases, was happy to let Horatio and Emma get on with their love affair and carried on living with them. Fanny was less happy about it, and she and Nelson eventually separated.

Emma and Horatio became the celebrity couple of the early 19th century, much to Fanny's horror. And they loved the publicity – they went on grand tours together and lapped up all the attention. In 1805, Lord Nelson led the English fleet into the Battle of Trafalgar and a great victory – but unfortunately he died in the process. After his death, Lord Nelson was an even bigger hero than before. They even built him a rather nice monument – Nelson's Column in Trafalgar Square – and named the London square after his battle. But Emma, the love of his life, was seen as a bit of an embarrassment. Even though Horatio had wanted Emma to inherit some of his wealth, she didn't get a penny. Ten years later, poor old Emma died in poverty.

Orpheus and Eurydice

This story from Greek mythology is another tragic love story (funny how they seldom end well).

Orpheus and Eurydice were a young married couple. One day Eurydice was bitten by a poisonous snake and died.

Orpheus was so heartbroken he travelled to the Underworld to try and get his wife back. He presented such a sad story to Hades, King of the Underworld, that Hades decided he would grant Orpheus's wish, but on one condition: that Orpheus did not look at Eurydice until they were back in the upper world.

You wouldn't have thought it would be too difficult, would you? But Orpheus couldn't help throwing a quick glance behind him just as they were almost out of the Underworld. Straight away, Eurydice was whisked off, leaving Orpheus to face life without her.

Potions

Love potions often feature in old stories and myths – usually, ones that don't end well. In the medieval story of Tristan and Isolde, for example, the pair drink a love potion by mistake and fall in love, but Isolde is already engaged and has to go ahead with the marriage. She and Tristan can't help but love each other because of the potion: eventually they both die of a broken heart.

If that doesn't put you off, here's a recipe for your own love potion – it really does work. Well, even if it doesn't, it tastes nice...

Passion potion

Ingredients (for two glasses):
2 posh glasses (ask first!)
Small amounts of runny honey
and sugar on separate saucers
About 200 ml of passion
fruit juice
About 100 ml of lemonade
Fresh mint leaves
A lemon

Mint leaves and/or strawberries and/or raspberries
To decorate:
Cocktail sticks (optional)
Posh ice cubes (optional – see below)
To make the potion:
1 Dip the rim of each glass into the honey, then dip
it into the sugar. Your glasses are now sugar-frosted.
2 Pour half the passion fruit juice into each glass.
3 Finely chop some mint leaves – about half a
teaspoonful – and add it to the fruit juice in
each glass.
4 Finely chop some lemon rind – about half a
teaspoonful – and add it to the fruit juice in each
glass. Make sure your lemon isn't the waxed kind,
and that its skin is clean.

5 Squeeze the juice of half the lemon and divide it between the glasses.

6 Top up with lemonade, being careful to leave room in the glass for decoration and/or ice cubes.

To decorate:

Here are a few ideas:

• Float some nice-looking mint leaves on top of the potion.

• Cut a couple of strawberries and/or raspberries down the middle and push them on to the rims of the glasses.

• Put some fruit on cocktail sticks and arrange them across the top of each glass.

• Use a potato peeler to cut a spiral of lemon peel and arrange that over the side of the glass.

To make posh ice cubes:

1 Half-fill an ice cube tray with water and float a slice of strawberry, a whole raspberry or a mint leaf in each compartment.

2 Put it in the freezer and wait until the ice is solid. (This might take a couple of hours.)

3 Fill the tray to the top with water and return it to the freezer.

4 When the ice is ready, you'll have really pretty ice cubes with a strawberry slice (or raspberry or mint leaf) floating in the middle.

You could also make pink ice cubes: fill your ice-cube tray with a mixture of half cranberry juice and half water.

A passion fruit superstition

If you kiss a passion fruit on 1 February your dreams will come true!

Quiz

How much do you know about love traditions and famous couples? Try this quiz and find out.

1 At weddings, it's traditional to wear something old, something new...
a) Something red that's made with glue
b) Something borrowed and something blue
c) Something pink and one odd shoe

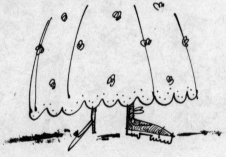

2 Who was Robin Hood's girlfriend?
a) Maid Marion
b) Maid Inengland
c) Maid Catherine

3 What did Shakespeare say was the "food of love"?

a) Oysters

b) Ice cream

c) Music

4 What precious stone is traditionally used in engagement rings?

a) Sapphire

b) Ruby

c) Diamond

5 Which couple were famous outlaws?

a) Ronald and Nancy Reagan

b) Bonnie and Clyde

c) Posh and Becks

6 What's the most popular Valentine's Day gift?

a) White roses

b) Red carnations

c) Red roses

7 The makers of the Barbie doll named Barbie and her boyfriend after their own children. What was the boyfriend's name?
a) Len
b) Den
c) Ken

8 Who is Mickey Mouse's girlfriend?
a) Minnie
b) Maxi
c) Winnie

9 On your wedding day, it's lucky to see a...
a) Rain cloud
b) White cloud
c) Rainbow

10 Which frog did Miss Piggy fancy?

a) Kermit
b) Freddy
c) Mr Toad

11 The person who catches the bride's bouquet is supposed to do what next?

a) Die
b) Marry
c) Divorce

12 Which superhero had a girlfriend called Mary Jane Watson?
a) Superman
b) Spider-man
c) Batman

13 Which famous general sent his wife a love letter complaining that she never wrote to him?
a) Napoleon
b) Alexander the Great
c) Montgomery

14 A superstition says that it's bad luck to include a particular flower in a wedding bouquet, because it's associated with death. Which one?

a) Sweet pea

b) Lily

c) Daisy

15 What do the bride and groom traditionally cut together on their wedding day?

a) The wedding cake

b) A ribbon declaring the marriage "open"

c) The bride's hair

Answers

1 b) 2 a) 3 c) 4 c) 5 b) 6 c) 7 c) 8 a) 9 c) 10 a) 11 b) 12 b) 13 a) 14 b) 15 a)

Romeo and Juliet

This Shakespeare play is one of the best-known love stories in the world. Like many love stories, it's a tale of woe...

Romeo and Juliet are young and in love and plan to get married, but there's a problem: their families hate each other. So Juliet's family arranges for her to be married off to someone else.

Not surprisingly, Juliet decides to try and avoid the wedding. She gets hold of a special sleeping potion that makes it seem as though she's dead, thoughtfully dashes off a note to Romeo telling him about it, then takes the potion. Romeo hears that Juliet has died but doesn't get her note.

He rushes to her tomb, sees her body and kills himself by drinking poison. Juliet wakes up, only to find Romeo dead beside her, and she kills herself with Romeo's dagger. So it all ends rather badly. (It sounds a bit like Antony and Cleopatra's story, doesn't it?)

The tale is such an enduring one that the play has been performed for centuries and has been made into films and musicals.

A strange Shakespearean fact

Shakespeare's play *Romeo and Juliet* is set in the Italian city of Verona. Every Valentine's Day, the city receives hundreds of valentine's cards addressed to Juliet!

Shah Jahan

A 17th-century Indian Moghul Emperor made sure that his own love story would be remembered far into the future...

♥♥ TRUE LOVE STORIES: Shah Jahan and Mumtaz Mahal

In 1612 Prince Khurram married the beautiful Arjumand Banu Begam. Theirs was a marriage of love – most royal marriages were made for political reasons. Arjumand was given a new name, Mumtaz Mahal, which means Chosen One of the Palace.

In 1627, Prince Khurram's father died and he became Emperor. By this time, he and Mumtaz had 13 children! Khurram changed his name to Shah Jahan, which means King of the World.

Sadly, three years later, Mumtaz died giving birth to their 14th child. Shah Jahan's heart was broken and it's said that his hair turned white overnight. He locked himself away in his room. When he came out, he decided to build his beloved wife the most beautiful and grand tomb in the world, made of gleaming white marble.

It took over 20,000 workers 22 years to build the amazing tomb. It's famous today, more than 350 years later, as the Taj Mahal in Agra, India.

Incredibly, Shah Jahan had plans for another Taj Mahal made from black marble to sit opposite the white one that would be his own tomb, but his plans were scuppered when he was put in prison by his own son! So both Mumtaz Mahal's and Shah Jahan's bodies lie together underneath the one Taj Mahal that did get built.

Sleepovers

If you're planning a sleepover with your best mates, here are a few tips:

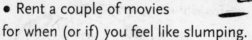

- Remove any little brothers who might try and sabotage the sleepover. You will have to get a parent to help with this.
- Rent a couple of movies for when (or if) you feel like slumping.
- Don't have some people on the floor and some on beds and sofas. If anyone has to go on the floor, everyone has to.
- Check that everyone has everything they need with

them (pyjamas, nightdresses, toothbrushes, etc) at the beginning of the evening – while there's still time to do something about it.
- Make sure you have plenty of games lined up – see page 36.
- Make sure there's plenty of food.

Perfect pizzas

Pizzas are classic sleepover food. Why not get all your friends to make their own pizza and choose their own toppings?

Ingredients:

Individual pizza bases (one for each sleepover guest)

Passata (available in supermarkets) or home-made tomato sauce

Toppings: choose from mozzarella cheese, cheddar cheese, tomato slices, slices of mushroom, olives, slices of pepperoni, chopped or sliced onion, sweetcorn, ham, part-cooked spinach, broccoli ... or anything else you fancy.

To make the pizzas:

1 Spread some passata or tomato sauce (not the kind you buy in bottles to go on your chips, though!) over the pizza base.

2 Choose some toppings to go on top – any combination you like.

3 Put the pizzas in the oven according to the instructions on the pizza bases. (You'll need an adult to do this bit.)

4 Feast on your delicious pizzas.

Chocolate strawberries

Ingredients:

Strawberries – enough for everyone to have four or five each

A large bar of plain chocolate (you might need more than one bar – it's best to stock up!)

Paper towels

To make the chocolate fruit:

1 Get an adult to do this bit: heat a saucepan of water on the cooker. When it starts to boil, reduce it to a simmer. Stand a bowl on top of the saucepan and heat the chocolate bar in the bowl until it melts.

It's important not to let the water boil, or the chocolate will get overheated and become lumpy.

2 Arrange the strawberries on paper towels, pointing upwards.

3 Take the bowl off the heat and spoon some melted chocolate over each strawberry. This can be a messy business.

4 Leave the chocolate to go hard.

5 Arrange the strawberries on a plate. You'll find that however many of these you make, there won't be enough.

Sleepover souvenirs

If you're having a sleepover on a special occasion, why not have some plain white T-shirts and fabric pens at the ready? Everyone can write or draw something on each T-shirt. When you've all finished, each guest will have a T-shirt to remember the evening by. (Whether they'll actually want to wear them is another matter!)

Tokens

It used to be traditional for boyfriends and girlfriends to give one another love tokens, but it's much less common today. Maybe some of these old love-token ideas should be brought back?

Flash cash

During the Middle Ages, a popular love token was a bent coin. (It doesn't sound very impressive, does it?) Coins that were bent in half were supposed to be lucky and bring you more money, but coins exchanged by lovers were bent into a cup shape.

The Victorians kept up this tradition but changed it a bit: they sanded down each side of a coin and engraved it with their names and love symbols like hearts, Cupid or flowers. Depending on how rich you were, you might give a copper, silver or gold coin. These coins were also exchanged between friends and relatives as well as lovers. We can't bring this custom back today, though: defacing a coin is against the law!

Special spoons

"Loving spoons" are a special Welsh tradition. Young men would carve a wooden spoon with delicate designs on the handle and a heart-shaped spoon bowl; then they would give it to girls they wanted to go out with. When Welsh actress Catherine Zeta-Jones got married to Michael Douglas, the couple were presented with a traditional Welsh loving spoon at their wedding.

If you don't fancy carving a wooden spoon, you might like to choose one of the other love tokens that have been popular at different times: lockets, handkerchiefs, ribbons or locks of hair, for example.

Under the mistletoe

Christmas often has one or two nasty surprises up its sleeve, and someone planting a damp smacker on you underneath the mistletoe is one of them. If you can, avoid mistletoe altogether but there are times when you won't be able to: at other people's houses, for example. The trick is not to be taken by surprise, so be on the alert, spot where the mistletoe is and keep away from it if you can.

Often mistletoe is placed above a doorway, so unless you want to stay in the same room, or gain entry via a window, you'll have to walk under it. Mistletoe kissers will probably be waiting expectantly nearby.

Unless you want to look like Ebeneezer Scrooge, you'll have no choice but to go along with it: in the unfortunate event you get caught, present your cheek first to avoid an unwelcome smacker on the lips.

Valentine's Day

The tradition of Valentine's Day began with the ancient Romans and a rather bizarre festival called Lupercalia. The fun included single women's names being put in a special urn to be picked out by the single men in a sort of romantic prize draw. Nobody knows how long the lucky (or unlucky) couples were supposed to spend together – let's hope it wasn't too long.

Lupercalia was outlawed by the pope in the fifth century AD and replaced with the feast of Saint Valentine. In fact, Saint Valentine is a bit of a mystery: he was either a priest in Rome, an Italian bishop or a saintly African man...

And his remains are said to be in various different parts of the world, including Scotland and Ireland!

From the fifteenth century onwards, it has become popular to send a valentine (a love note or poem, or nowadays a card) to someone you like or fancy, and Valentine's Day has become a potentially cringe-making time of year.

Make sure you don't go anywhere near a restaurant on Valentine's Day – you'll be surrounded by mushy couples having slushy dinners for two and snogging all over the place. In fact, it's probably best not to go out on Valentine's evening at all.

Vanilla Valentine Cookies

Why not avoid the snogging and get your friends over for the evening in on Valentine's Day? As a special treat for your mates, try these simple pink vanilla cookies...

You need:

225 g plain white flour

75 g butter or margarine

75 g caster sugar

1 beaten egg

half a teaspoon vanilla essence

few drops of red food colouring

a cookie cutter – heart-shaped if you can find one

A greased baking sheet

An adult

To make the cookies:

1 Get your adult to preheat the oven to 180oC/Mark 4.

2 Sift the flour into a bowl and rub the butter or marg into it, until the mixture looks a bit like breadcrumbs.

3 Stir in the sugar, beaten egg, vanilla essence and just one or two drops of food colouring. Mix it together into pink dough.

4 Sprinkle some flour onto a work surface and roll

out the cookie dough until it's about half a centimetre thick.

5 Prick the dough all over with a fork and use your cookie-cutter to cut out cookie shapes.

6 Put the cookies as far apart as possible on the baking sheet.

7 Get your adult to put it in the oven.

8 Bake for about ten minutes, till the cookies are light brown. Then get your adult to take them out of the oven.

9 Let them cool a bit, then get your adult to put them on a wire tray.

10 When they're cool, put them on a plate and feed your friends.

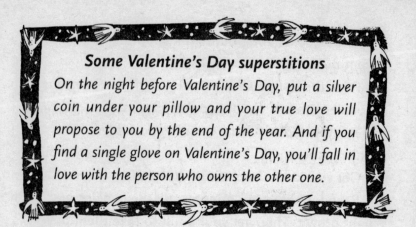

Some Valentine's Day superstitions

On the night before Valentine's Day, put a silver coin under your pillow and your true love will propose to you by the end of the year. And if you find a single glove on Valentine's Day, you'll fall in love with the person who owns the other one.

Birds and animals seem to be very important on Valentine's Day:

If you see a squirrel it means...

you'll marry a miser.

If you see a goldfinch...

you'll marry someone very rich.

If you see a
flock of doves...

 you'll have a happy marriage.

If you see a robin...

 you'll marry a sailor.

If you see a sparrow...

 you'll marry someone
poor – but you'll be happy.

Slushy Valentine fact
You can send your valentine's card to Loveland,
Colorado so that it gets a postmark from the
romantically named town.

Venus
See *Aphrodite*.

Weddings

Long ago, people getting married were thought to be especially prone to attack from evil spirits! So lots of superstitions grew up around weddings:

- Chimney sweeps are supposed to be lucky, and seeing one on the way to a wedding is said to bring good luck for the marriage. Even today it's possible to hire a chimney sweep to come to your wedding!

- If the bride and groom see one another before the ceremony on the wedding day, it's bad luck. Most people who get married follow this superstition.

- It's a bad sign if you see a monk, a nun, a pig or a hare on the way to the wedding, but it's good luck to see a lamb, a toad, a dove or a spider.

• It's also good luck to see a spider on your wedding dress or veil (though you might not think so if you're arachnophobic). It means you'll be rich.

• It's supposed to be bad luck if the bride trips when she goes into her house for the first time after she's married. That's how the tradition of the groom carrying the bride over the threshold started. An old Scottish tradition is for the groom's mother to break shortbread over the bride's head as she's carried over the threshold!

• An old custom was for guests to throw shoes at the married couple for good luck!

• The strangest superstition of all is giving your cat its food in your left shoe a week before your wedding! It's supposed to bring good fortune – even though it ruins your shoes.

A strange wedding fact

It's quite common for brides to throw their wedding bouquet over their shoulder – whoever catches it is supposed to be the next to marry. But in days gone by the bride used to throw an old shoe – it's amazing anyone stood around waiting to catch it!

Looking for Mr Right

Girls – want to know who's going to be your husband? Simply try one of these five tried and tested methods and he'll appear in your dreams:

- Rub your headboard with lemon peel before you turn out the light.
- Put daisies under your pillow.
- Put a sprig of rosemary in one shoe and a sprig of thyme in the other. Put the shoes at the end of your bed. (If this doesn't work, it might at least make those pongy old trainers smell a bit better.)
- Wear your nightie inside out.
- Put a mirror under your pillow. (Which might be a bit uncomfortable.)

And if you're wondering whether you're going to fall in love soon, find a mule with long ears and ask it. (Obviously!) The mule will understand perfectly. If its answer is yes, it will shake its head.

If you say yes, I'll give you this carrot

If it moves one ear, that means maybe. And if the mule doesn't move at all, that means no.

Worldwide weddings

Once you've found the person you're going to marry, you'll be interested to know that it's good luck to propose marriage on a Friday evening. Then you'll want to start planning your wedding. Why not incorporate one of these unusual wedding rituals from around the world?

- Egyptian women pinch the bride on her wedding day for good luck!

C'mon if you think you're hard enough

pinch pinch pinch pinch pinch

- Fijian grooms present the bride's father with a whale's tooth.
- In Korea, ducks form part of the wedding procession! Because they mate for life, they're a symbol of fidelity.

- Danish brides are kissed by all the men at the wedding reception when the groom leaves the room. When the bride leaves the room, the groom gets the same treatment from all the women.
- The Karo people of Ethiopia tattoo the bride-to-be's stomach!

Xs

Have you ever wondered why we use an "X" to represent a kiss? It's supposed to come from medieval times, when people who couldn't read and write signed their names as "X". They would often kiss the "X" to show their sincerity ... and over time it came to represent the kiss rather than the signature.

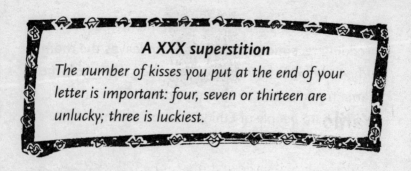

A XXX superstition

The number of kisses you put at the end of your letter is important: four, seven or thirteen are unlucky; three is luckiest.

Xochiquetzal

Xochiquetzal is the Aztec goddess of love and beauty. Her name means "flower feather" (which is a bit easier to say), and she's followed about by birds and flowers wherever she goes. Every eight years, the Aztecs in Mexico held a feast in honour of Xochiquetzal, where they would wear animal and flower masks.

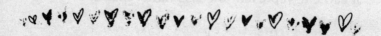

Yarilo

Yarilo is an old Slavic god of
love and growth (Slavic
countries include Bulgaria
and Romania, among
others). You'll be able to
spot Yarilo by his blond
hair, white clothing, bare feet,
crown of flowers and the fact that he'll be riding a
white horse. Oh, and he'll probably be holding some
wheat and a human skull, too.

On his feast day of 4 June, a statue of Yarilo used
to be put in a coffin and carried through towns and
villages at sunset, while women would cry and
lament. Then the coffin was buried and everyone
would cheer up and have a huge party. It doesn't
sound like much of a feast day for Yarilo, does it?
But at least everyone else had a good time.

Zoria

Zoria is an old Slavic goddess of love and beauty.
She's also associated with the dawn, and opens the
gates for the sun's chariot to ride across the sky at
daybreak. Her sister, also called Zoria, helpfully
shuts the gates after the sun in the evening.

Have an **Absolutely Brilliant** Chummy Day with your Excellent Friends

Also in the A–Z series...

Find out:

- how to build a snowman, stage a nativity play and other Christmas essentials

- the truth about sprouts

- some weird Christmas traditions you might want to try ... and a few you certainly won't

Also in the A–Z series...

Find out:

- how to trick or treat, carve a pumpkin and other scary essentials

- what to do if you meet a werewolf

- some terrifying tales you might believe ... and a few you certainly won't